The Schoolhouse

By

Jill Watson Glassco

LHP

The Schoolhouse

Published by:
LifeHouse Publishing
P.O. Box 2825
Peoria, Arizona 85380
www.lifehousepub.com

ISBN 978-0-9839409-3-7

All quoted Scriptures and paraphrased passages are taken from the NEW AMERICAN STANDARD BIBLE®, Copyright © 1960, 1962, 1963, 1968, 1971, 1972, 1973, 1975, 1977, 1995 by The Lockman Foundation. Used by permission.

Author's Note

My grandmother, Elsie Thomas Brazelle, was born March 25, 1896, in Sweetens Cove, Tennessee, the youngest of N. Floyd and Abbie Thomas' nine children. In 1904, the Thomas family moved to a farm in Rankin Cove on the Tennessee River near Jasper. Floyd, a cobbler by trade, indentured a young man to work the farm while he made shoes for the local community and also shipped his goods to New York, London, and Paris. Abbie, a mid-wife and herb doctor, served the sick throughout their rural neighborhood. During her absence, a housekeeper cared for the children and performed the daily chores.

After graduating from high school in 1916, Elsie received her first teaching assignment: a one-room, eight-grade schoolhouse nestled in the picturesque mountains of east Tennessee.

In 1955, Grandmother Brazelle wrote a detailed letter to her daughter, Verna (my mother), describing her adventures as that young teacher in the backwoods of the Appalachians. In her letter, Grandmother encouraged Mother to turn those adventures into a short story and submit it for publication. While my mother never attempted that assignment, she passed on to me the handwritten record of this beautiful, true tale of faith, determination, danger, servitude, and love.

From a heart-dream conceived years ago, comes *The Schoolhouse*, a story/work book birthed through that courageous teacher's granddaughter. It is my hope that my grandmother's story will encourage you to depend more deeply on God, inspire you to persevere through difficult circumstances, and motivate you to finish life strong.

Jill Watson Glassco

Note: Fictitious names and details are added to replace lost details of Grandmother's story.

Contents

Chapter 1
The Assignment

My bare feet hit the wooden floor in eagerness to prepare for the day's travel as soft hues of pinks and violets painted the skyline. The dawn air felt warm on that summer morning in 1916.

The long-awaited letter from the county superintendent had arrived the week before, confirming my first teaching position at a small school tucked back in the woods on Whitwell Mountain. This assignment to teach first through eighth graders spanned from July through December—a shortened term due to severe Tennessee winters and the need for children to help with farming in the spring and early summer.

All my life I had dreamed of becoming a schoolteacher. Although that dream was coming true, my spirits spiraled when I recalled the discouraging words from Clara Hill, a former teacher at that mountain school.

"Please don't accept that location," Miss Hill said. "You'll never finish the term. No one can. A teacher hasn't completed an assignment there in over four years. I tried last year only to give up and come home. Elsie, the students are disobedient and there's an unbalanced boy who… well, let me just say you'll face other problems, too."

I had learned to turn to the Word of God for encouragement when life got hard, and for instruction when I didn't know what to do. Before dressing, I picked up my small, leather Bible on the nightstand and sat down in a rocker by the window.

My favorite Sunday school teacher, Mr. Rawtin, gave me that treasured book on Christmas Day when I was six years old, as a reward for good attendance.

"Dear Lord, I need help," I prayed. "You know I've dreamed of bein' a teacher since I was a little girl. I believe You planted that dream in my heart. But why, Lord, have You assigned me to such a difficult place?"

A breeze through the open window cast a loose strand of my light brown hair across my face. Brushing it aside, I opened my Bible to Nehemiah 4:14 and read, "*Do not be afraid of them; remember the Lord who is great and awesome, and fight for your... sons and your daughters.*"

Those powerful words refueled my determination to chase my dream. "Lord, forgive me for focusin' on my own abilities and not *Yours*," I said aloud. "I *can* do all things through You who gives me strength (Phil. 4:13). I have no intention of bein' the fifth teacher to quit and, with Your guidance, I know I can handle this assignment."

My parents remained quiet as our wagon bumped down the lane from our farm in Rankin Cove, my home since childhood, to the nearest train depot.

"Do your best, sweetheart," Papa said with a smile and an affectionate pat on my head.

"Elsie, please be careful and take good care of yourself," Mama said softly. It was hard for her to let me, the baby of nine children, leave home.

I kissed Mama's tear-moistened cheek, hugged Papa, and in a tug o' war between anticipation and reservation, boarded the early morning train bound for the station in Whitwell.

The shrill blast of the engine whistle sounded within moments of my settling into the first available window seat. With a jerk and a lurch, the locomotive inched forward and gradually gained speed. The click-clack-click of the wheels along the rails and rhythmic sway of the coach calmed me. Imaginations of days to come played across my mind as I looked out on the fertile valley. An emerald streak of rich foliage, the fruit of frequent summer showers, raced by as the train moved steadily down the tracks. Before it seemed possible, the conductor announced, "Coming into Whitwell. Coming into Whitwell."

Struggling to carry two heavy bags swollen with clothes, books, and personal items, I trudged toward the nearby livery stable to hire a carriage to take me the rest of my journey: a distance of five or six miles up the mountain. At the base of the mountain sat an incline tram with bucket seats to carry miners up to the coal mines and small cars with benches for other passengers. The stable owner told me the incline was dangerous and very few people risked taking it, especially women. Thankfully, an available buggy allowed me to avoid the hazardous tram and Phillip Laney, a rather tall and handsome young man, offered to be my driver.

Two chestnut-colored steeds drew our carriage up the steep mountainside. The mid-afternoon air felt fresh and a forest in full regalia adorned both sides of the winding trail. Sparrows, cardinals, and an occasional yellow finch darted from tree to tree while squirrels, too numerous to count, scampered along the road. The beautiful scenery paired with pleasant conversation made me forget the problems I might later face.

After an hour's ride, the driver halted the carriage in front of a home where he suggested I might find room and board. An appealing bungalow rested in a large yard with enough trees to afford plenty of shade. At one side of the yard stood a grocery and dry goods store where the family that owned the house earned their living. On the other side of the cottage lay a lovely vegetable and flower garden arrayed with white daisies and tall, yellow sunflowers that nodded their heads when the wind stirred. Trails of morning glories, as blue as the July sky, zigzagged in and out of the long rows of corn stalks and snap beans.

A friendly couple in their late thirties, along with their four daughters ranging in age from seven to sixteen, stepped out to greet us. James and Naomi Graham gladly accepted me as a boarder and Mr. Graham lifted my luggage from the back of the carriage. Eager to see where I'd be teaching, I left my things sitting on their front porch and rode with Mr. Laney a few more miles down the road to the school, a distance I would be walking to and from every weekday. Being reared on a farm, the thought of long walks didn't really bother me.

We found the small, but well-built schoolhouse located alongside the road in a grove of towering trees. Oaks, hickories, and dogwoods provided an awning over the building as well as the playground. This picturesque location commanded the only appropriate name for that school: "Shady Grove." The quietness, save for the songs of birds and chattering of squirrels, filled me with peace and under my breath I said, *"You will make known to me the path of life; in Your presence is fullness of joy: in Your right hand there are pleasures forever"* (Ps. 16:11).

The interior of the single-room school was well kept and clean. Strong, solid desks for the children stood in straight rows like soldiers in marching formation and a potbelly stove sat in one back corner. Freshly painted walls supported an open ceiling exposing large hand-hewn oak beams.

The thrill of standing in *my* very own classroom helped to ease my feelings of discouragement from the earlier warnings. With God's help, I could… no, I *would* be the first teacher in over four years to complete the five-month school term.

Reflections #1

POINTS to ponder

1. Choose one. When things get hard, I turn to:

   a. My friends

   b. My family

   c. Myself

   d. God

   e. I don't have anyone to turn to.

2. What was Elsie's dream? _____ What is your dream that may seem impossible to others?_____

3. What obstacles are standing between you and your dream?_____
   _____

   What do you believe God is saying about your dream?_____
   _____

PEARLS from God's heart to yours

_____ (your name), I love you with a love that will never end. I want you to be close to Me (Jer. 31:3).

_____ (your name), I have plans for you to give you a future and hope. When you talk to Me, I listen. When you look for Me with all your heart, you will find Me and the plans I have for you (Jer. 29:11-13).

Don't be afraid, _____ (your name), I am your God. I will strengthen you and help you. I am holding you in My hands (Isa. 41:10).

PETITIONS from your heart to Jesus

_____

_____

_____

Chapter 2
Mrs. Graham's Warning

"Good luck, Miss Thomas," Mr. Laney said as I climbed down from the buggy when we got back to my new home. "I'll be happy to give you a ride any time you need one. G'bye, ma'am," he said and then snapped the reins to start the horses.

"Thank you very much for your help," I called back with a smile and a wave as the carriage moved slowly down the dusty road.

"Supper's ready, Elsie."

I turned to see Mrs. Graham standing on the front porch. Her auburn hair combed neatly back into a braid at the base of her slender neck revealed her attractive face. Her welcoming smile made me believe I already had a friend in these unfamiliar surroundings.

"I've got a surprise for you," she said, using a corner of her apron to wipe beads of perspiration from her forehead. "We picked up another boarder while you visited Shady Grove. She'll be teachin' at the school over yonder on Kelly Creek where my girls go."

The screen door swung open and Gladys Wear, my high school friend, rushed toward me with outstretched arms. Returning her hug, I looked up and whispered, "Thank You, Lord Jesus."

The aroma of fried chicken, mashed potatoes, and hot biscuits made my mouth water as we walked arm in arm into the house for supper. A long table donning a blue-checkered tablecloth and eight place settings furnished the roomy kitchen. Mr. Graham sat in a sturdy armchair at the head of the table, and Mrs. Graham, in a matching seat, sat at the foot. Benches along each side provided ample space for the Graham girls, Gladys, and me. After joining hands, Mr. Graham prayed, "Lord, thank You for this meal we're about to receive and bless the hands that prepared it. Please bless this food to the nourishment of our bodies and our bodies to Thy service. Thank You, Lord, for these good teachers You've sent to Marion County to sit at our table and to teach the children. Amen."

Gladys and I enjoyed getting acquainted with the Grahams. The four girls asked an endless number of questions during the delicious meal. After helping wash the dishes, the sisters insisted on taking us on a walk while Mrs. Graham finished cleaning up.

A well-worn path behind their house led us through the woods to a great cavern. "That's Devil's Den," the girls said in unison. Mary Grace, the seven-year-old, tossed a stone into the seemingly bottomless black chasm. The resounding echoes continued for several seconds after the pebble struck what must have been boulders jutting out along the walls of the cave.

The oldest sister, Rebecca, whispered, "Many men have entered Devil's Den never to be seen again. Papa says when nighttime falls over the mountain, you can hear moans of those lost souls coming up from their stony graves."

With a little shiver, I followed the children and Gladys farther up the path until we reached a rock bluff overlooking the tiny mining town of Whitwell. Layers of mountain peaks edged the landscape, and the crimson sun meeting the horizon forged a gilded frame for deep purple clouds. Twinkling lights peeped through the windows of the homes below as moonlight replaced the light of day. The view was both breathtaking and comforting.

Gladys broke the peaceful silence. "It's gettin' dark," she said. "We better get back to the house before y'all's mama gets worried."

Reluctant to leave the serenity of the overlook, I took my time getting up from the rock where I'd been sitting, and we retraced our steps back to the Grahams' cottage.

The following day, the entire household attended Sunday school and church. After the service, Mr. and Mrs. Graham invited a number of young people from their congregation over to meet Gladys and me. I felt my cheeks flush when Phillip Laney arrived among the guests. Everyone seemed to have fun playing games and singing hymns around the family's old upright piano.

"Elsie, will you help me in the flower garden?" Mrs. Graham asked after most of the visitors had left.

As soon as we were outside, she said, "I don't want to frighten you, but there's something I need to tell you before you make the walk to school in the mornin'. On this mountain lives a woman who says she's bewitched. She wears long sticks in her ears and carries a large butcher knife and a club. Even though she lives twenty miles back on the mountain, she's been seen on this road and people say she's gettin' dangerous. Her family tries to confine her, but she often gets away. Your school's on the route she takes when she escapes. I must warn you to be very cautious and keep a sharp watch. At the first glimpse of her, you take to the woods, hide behind the trees 'til she passes, and then run as fast as you can to the nearest house."

Feeling overcome with fear, I choked back tears and said nothing except that I appreciated the information and her kindness. Because Mrs. Graham seemed so genuinely concerned, I trusted her advice and was already beginning to love her.

That night, Gladys and I retired early after supper to the room we shared. I slipped my little Bible out of the satchel I had packed for school the next day. Ghostly shadows danced on the wall from the flickering flame of the kerosene lantern. The lamplight illuminated these words printed in my beloved testament: "*Do not fear or be dismayed; tomorrow go out to face them, for the Lord is with you*" *(2 Chron. 20:17b).*

I spent much of the night in thought and prayer. When I did sleep, knives, bloody clubs, and people with horns haunted my dreams. I awoke at daybreak, however, feeling less afraid and resolved to do the work set before me with God ever by my side. After a hearty breakfast and yet another warning from my dear landlady, I began my lonely journey to the school, walking rapidly with great caution down the deserted road.

Reflections #2

POINTS to ponder

1. What two things did Elsie do when she was afraid? _____

_____

2. What are you facing now that frightens you? _____

_____

Is your dreaded fear a "what if" situation or reality? _____

_____

3. Read Psalm 56:3 and Proverbs 3:5-6. What does the Bible tell us to do when we feel frightened or overwhelmed? _____ God.

PEARLS from God's heart to yours

_____ (your name), I will never leave you nor forsake you. I am your Helper so do not be afraid (Heb. 13:5b-6).

_____ (your name), without Me you can do nothing (John 15:5) but through Me who gives you strength, you can do all things (Phil. 4:13).

_____ (your name), I will cover you with my feathers, and under My wings you may seek refuge, My faithfulness is a shield…you will not be afraid of the terror by night, or of the arrow that flies by day (Ps. 91:4-5).

PETITIONS from your heart to Jesus

_____

_____

_____

Chapter 3
First Day of School

SNAP! The loud crack of a stick breaking in the woods behind me made my heart leap. I whirled around just in time to catch a glimpse of the white tail of a young buck shooting into the forest like a racehorse out of the gate. Exhaling the breath I was subconsciously holding, I resumed my rapid pace, eager to reach my destination. Every sudden movement of a chipmunk or a bird sent me high-tailing it toward the nearest bush or tree to hide until I made certain the bewitched woman wasn't nearby.

With great relief, I finally reached the first house along the road and found a group of children gathered to walk to school. I later learned that families sent some of the larger boys to walk with the children who were frightened by talk of the witch.

"Good mornin', children," I said in a feigned strong voice. "I'm Miss Thomas, your new teacher."

"Good mornin', Miss Thomas," the boys and girls replied.

Several of the youngsters stood bare-footed. Most of the boys dressed in well-worn overalls carefully patched by loving hands, while cotton print dresses made from the material of used flour sacks clad many of the little girls. Their curious eyes and innocent faces captivated me.

"May I walk with you to Shady Grove?" I asked.

"Yes ma'am," they said enthusiastically. Together we reached the school safely and, to my satisfaction, on time. We joined a number of children on the playground who arrived earlier, and welcomed other students who soon appeared.

I walked up the front steps, pulled the skeleton key from my skirt pocket, and unlocked the door at Shady Grove. Albert, one of the older boys, helped me open the windows to let in fresh air and a breeze on that hot first day of school.

"For now, sit down at any desk, children. We'll get organized by age and grade later."

The children scrambled to desks; several competed for front desks but a few ambled toward the seats in the back of the room. I picked up a piece of chalk and wrote on the blackboard from Matt. 7:12: **In everything, treat people the same way you want them to treat you.**

"Raise your hand if you can tell me who spoke these wise words."

Several hands went up. "Yes, young man, you in the second row," I said, pointing to a lanky lad about nine or ten years old. "Tell me your name, please, before answering my question."

"My name's Henry Johnson, ma'am, and our president, Mr. Woodrow Wilson, spoke them good words," Henry said with a smile of confidence.

"Quiet," I said firmly to silence the children's snickers. "Thank you for your effort, Henry. The correct grammar is 'spoke *those* good words' and the correct answer is Jesus Christ spoke these words in His Sermon on the Mount in the Gospel of Matthew, the first book of the New Testament in the Holy Bible. His Golden Rule, as it's called, is goin' to be our rule at Shady Grove. We will *not* laugh at each other's mistakes. We *will* help and encourage one another. Is that understood?"

"Yes, Miss Thomas," came the sheepish reply in chorus.

Following the agenda I prepared the day before, I took roll, organized the children by age and grade, and then issued books. I felt pleased with the cooperation and good behavior of my twenty-seven students. However, when a man rode up on horseback to speak with me about his children, more than half of the boys and girls left their seats and ran to the door to listen. Therefore, additional classroom rules and manners turned out to be our first lesson that day; lessons in reading and writing followed.

Feeling quite proud of myself, I thought, "The past four teachers, poor dears, must not have known how to establish a firm hand of discipline." Just when that prideful notion swelled my brain to the point of popping, a loud commotion of barking and clucking erupted on the schoolyard. Before I could close the door, a brood of laying hens scurried into the classroom with a redbone hound in hot pursuit.

My orderly classroom morphed into a chaotic circus. Children jumped from their seats, laughing as they ran after the animals, while three of the little girls climbed up on top of their desks, squealing in fright. Books flew to the floor, scattered by the swift wags of the dog's powerful tail as he hurdled seats,

determined to catch one of his squawking prey. A feather floated past my nose and almost into my mouth as I yelled, "Get those chickens and that dog out of here!"

By the time our room cleared of fowls and hound, the tidy classroom lay in complete disarray. Over the next thirty minutes, my students and I swept feathers from the floor, picked up books, and re-aligned desks and chairs.

When lunchtime arrived, I dismissed the students to the playground to eat food they brought from home. My stomach growled. I looked forward to eating the hard-boiled eggs and yellow apple picked from Mrs. Graham's June apple tree. But before I could join the children outdoors, Albert's little sister, Katie, ran through the door crying, "Albert and Dan are fightin'!"

Grabbing two towels from a stack beside the washbowl, I rushed outside to confront the boys, both taller than me, wrestling fiercely on the ground.

"Albert! Dan! Stop it!" I ordered as they continued to roll about in the dust.

I thought, "Now what do I do, Lord?" Out of the corner of my eye I spotted a half-filled bucket under an oak tree the man visiting earlier had filled with water for his horse. I emptied the bucket on the boys' heads and said again, "Stop it, boys!"

I thanked God when the wrestlers responded to my last command, let go of the iron grips they had on each other, and clambered to their feet.

"Girls, give me two of your jump ropes," I said. "Dan and Albert, hold out your right fists."

All eyes focused on me. I almost chuckled at the puzzled looks on the faces of my students, but kept a stern composure as I wrapped Albert's right hand in a bulky towel and tied it in place with a jump rope. I then bound up Dan's hand in like manner. I had watched my mother discipline my older brothers this way when they got into scraps.

"Listen to me, boys. The good Lord crafted hands into instruments to praise Him, tools to help others, and machines to work the land. God did *not* fashion hands for us to hit each other. Your hands misbehaved today, so they'll have to sit a spell in those dressings. When I think they've had time to recover, I'll remove the ropes and towels. Now, go eat your lunches and no more fightin'. Do you understand?"

"Yes'm," said Albert.

"Yes, teacher," said Dan.

After lunch, I gave my students arithmetic assignments and then played games with them to help me remember their names. Exhausted, I decided to dismiss the children early.

I dropped to my knees beside my bed before going to sleep that night and rested my weary head against the feather mattress. One day of school lay behind me, but five long months stretched out before me.

"O Lord, I confess that I was prideful today and thought I was better than the past four teachers. Father, now I recognize *my own* shortcomings and realize I've got a lot to learn about teachin' children. How will I ever make it through this school term?" I prayed.

The Comforter's gentle voice resounded deep in my spirit and rekindled His strength within me by saying, *"My grace is sufficient for you, for (My) power is perfected in weakness"* *(2 Cor. 12:9).*

With renewed hope, I slipped on my cotton nightgown, crawled into bed, and fell asleep as soon as my head hit the goose-down pillow.

Reflections #3

POINTS to ponder

1. What was Elsie's prideful thought?_____

2. Read Isa. 14:12-15. The angel Lucifer committed the first sin. Where? _____

    Name the sin: _____   Read Rev. 12: 9. Prideful Lucifer became the _____.

3. Read Phil. 2:5-11. Jesus humbled Himself in obedience to God the Father. Is humility a

    sign of weakness or strength?_____   Pride is unwise sin that puffs up self and

    separates you from God. Humility, on the other hand, is wisely obeying and submitting to

    God while honoring others more than _____ .

PEARLS from God's heart to yours

_____ (your name), pride goes before destruction, and a haughty spirit before
stumbling (Prov. 16:18).

_____ (your name), I resist the proud but I give grace to the humble. Therefore,
humble yourself under My mighty hand and I will lift you up at the proper time (1 Pet. 5:5-6).

_____ (your name), a portion of the fruit of My Spirit is humility
(Gal. 5:22-23).

PETITIONS from your heart to Jesus

_____

_____

_____

_____

Chapter 4
The Intruder

*T*o my delight, the next couple of weeks ran more smoothly. I saw no sign of the bewitched stranger on my walks to or from school, there were no more surprise visits from farm animals, and my students quickly settled into the routine of school, so my fears seemed unfounded and the burden of anxiety I carried, eased.

"Students, today we're goin' to talk about Tennessee's history in the Civil War. Raise your hand if…." I stopped midsentence when a tall, robust boy charged into our schoolroom. The young man appeared to be around sixteen. He had unkempt, bushy hair and bulging pockets filled with, what turned out to be, hickory nuts and marbles.

Glancing around the room and not speaking a word, he dashed into the cloakroom grinning from ear to ear. Using the shelves as a ladder, the barefoot teen effortlessly climbed into the open rafters and perched on a crossbeam over my desk.

Too stunned to move, my eyes remained glued on the intruder as Miss Hill's warning of an "unbalanced boy" replayed in my mind.

What happened next caught me completely off guard. The boy reached into a pocket of his faded dungarees, pulled out a fist full of nuts and marbles, and then began throwing them at the children.

"Young man, you stop that and come down from there this instant," I said, jumping aside as a marble whizzed by, narrowly missing my head and cracking the slate board lying on my desk.

"Does anyone know who he is?" I frantically asked the children.

"He's Will Robison, teacher," Ben, one of my eighth graders, said. "He lives about a mile from here."

"Quick, Ben, go fetch his father. Children, go out on the playground. Hurry!"

No sooner had the children cleared the classroom, than Will climbed down from his battle station and followed the boys and girls outside. Picking up a ball and bat on the ground by the front steps, he ran, whooping and hollering, to the first base on the school's makeshift baseball field.

"Miss Thomas, Will loves to play ball," Oliver Beason said.

"Well then, go play ball 'til his father gets here," I said.

The boys scrambled onto the field and divided into teams. Oliver took Will by the arm and led him to home plate.

"You bat first, Will," Oliver said.

Will took his stance with eyes on the pitcher and the bat lifted over his right shoulder. CRACK! On the first pitch, he sent the ball sailing into left field and ran with a reckless gait to first base, yelling with glee every step of the way.

Tears stung my eyes. "O dear Lord, he just wants… to *play,*" I whispered to God.

I watched with curiosity when a younger boy stepped up to hit. This batter swung at the first two pitches but missed. Will jumped up and down waving his arms and laughing. When the bat finally connected with the ball on the third pitch, Will hooted like a screech owl and took off running back toward home plate. Johnny, the first baseman, ran after Will. But instead of trying to get him out, he grabbed his arm and yelled, "Other way, Will." Johnny turned Will in the direction of second base and gave him a light push.

Will jogged on as fast as his clumsy legs would go. So went the game—every boy helped Will do what he was supposed to do and get where he was supposed to go. I admired my students for treating this boy, who seemed to step through life to the beat of a different drummer, [1] with grace and compassion.

By and by, Will's father arrived. He apologized to me for his boy getting away and coming to the school.

"We'll try our best, ma'am, to keep him home," he said.

"Mr. Robison, we have recess everyday around 12:30. Why don't you bring Will to Shady Grove from time to time to play ball with the boys?" I suggested.

---

[1] Henry David Thoreau, *Walden* (Boston, MA: Beacon Press, 1997), 305.

Will nodded his head as though understanding, and a big smile of satisfaction spread across his freckled face. The pair left the schoolyard and disappeared down the path cutting through the woods to their cabin.

"Do you know the Robison family?" I asked Mrs. Graham as I helped her clear dishes from the supper table that evening.

"Yes, Jessilee Robison and I went to school together. The Robisons keep to themselves most of the time because of their son Will, but they're good folks—hardworking and kind."

"Do you think Mrs. Robison would mind me visiting sometime?" I asked. "I'd like to take her one of the primary books for Will. With help, I think he might learn his ABC's and maybe even learn to write his name."

"Elsie, that's a wonderful idea," Mrs. Graham said, her blue eyes sparkling. "I'll go with you and take Jessilee one of my famous deep-dish apple cobblers. Now, let's just let the angels dry these dishes and go see what Gladys and the girls are up to."

We joined the family on the front porch, and I sat down in the swing with ten-year-old Sarah. Delicate silver moonlight spilled over the treetops, and a canopy of glimmering stellar jewels covered the night sky. Whippoorwills, crickets, and katydids crooned a moonlight sonata across Whitwell Mountain.

"Lord Jesus," I prayed silently, "Your brother James told us, *'...Do not hold your faith in our glorious Lord Jesus Christ with an attitude of personal favoritism' (James 2:1).* Thank You for the lesson You taught me through my students today: to treat every person with kindness and grace. Please forgive me for misjudging Will Robison. Lord, bless the Robisons, help Will to be all You created him to be, and enable him to fulfill Your purposes on this earth."

My focus turned to Mr. Graham's deep baritone voice as he sang:

> *"The Savior comes and walks with me, and sweet communion here have we;*
>
> *He gently leads me with His hand, for this is heaven's borderland.*
>
> *O Beulah land, sweet Beulah land, as on Thy highest mount I stand,*
>
> *I look away across the sea, where mansions are prepared for me,*
>
> *And view the shining glory shore, my heaven, my home forevermore."* [2]

---

[2] BEULAH LAND, Words, Edgar Page Stites, 1876. Tune, Jno. R. Sweney, 1878.

Reflections #4

POINTS to ponder

1. How did Elsie's students treat Will? _____ How do you treat people who are different than you?_____

2. Read Matt. 7:1-2. Who spoke these words? _____ What do you think Jesus meant?_____

3. Read Luke 10:30-37. What opportunities do you have to be a "good Samaritan" to someone who is different than you? _____

PEARLS from God's heart to yours

_____ (your name), happy are those who are kind to others for they shall also receive kindness (Matt. 5:7).

_____ (your name), while you have the opportunity, do good to all people, and especially to other Christians (Gal. 6:10).

_____ (your name), I will not forget your work and the love you show in My name (Heb. 6:10).

PETITIONS from your heart to Jesus

_____

_____

_____

_____

Chapter 5
Witch in the Schoolyard

At the beginning of the school term, I went home a couple of times to visit my parents on our farm near Jasper, partly because I missed my family and partly because I enjoyed those long carriage rides with Phillip Laney. The Grahams and Gladys quickly became my second family; so as the weeks passed, I rarely traveled back to Rankin Cove. Phillip, however, continued to drive up the mountain every now and then to jokingly ask me, "Did you order a ride, ma'am?"

On Saturdays, Gladys and I liked going sightseeing in Marion County with our new friends from church. We often walked along the rocky bluffs overlooking Whitwell or explored the intriguing coal mines tunneling deep into the mountain. Those fun summer weeks soon slipped into cooler, shorter fall days.

Splashes of red, yellow, and orange brushed over the green canvas of the Appalachian mountainsides. Goldenrods and black-eyed Susans lined the roads and flocks of birds migrating south for the winter filled the bright blue autumn skies. School progressed well, life seemed gratifying, and thoughts of the witch rarely troubled my mind.

One morning in late September, a movement outside the classroom caught my attention as I walked from desk to desk checking the children's work. Through the doorway, I saw a slender figure running toward the school. The woman repeatedly hacked the air with a butcher knife gripped tightly in her right hand. She clutched a wooden club in her other hand, and sticks about five inches long protruded from each ear.

I dashed to the door to close and lock it. Thankfully, she could not see in the high windows opened only at the top.

"Be very quiet," I said to the children, and then I silently prayed, "God, You are our refuge and strength, a very present help in trouble (Ps. 46:1). Please help us, Lord Jesus."

My students sat in total silence; no one moved. Heavy footsteps pounded the stairs and stopped on the front landing of the schoolhouse. She tried the door handle, shaking it violently, and then stomped back down the steps when it did not open. Several tense minutes passed, and

I thought she had gone until shadows reappeared through the crack under the door. The strange woman began to push twigs and leaves under the threshold into the schoolroom. The children remained perfectly still.

Her shadow disappeared again, and we all sat motionless for some time. Rising quietly, I climbed onto a stool, peered out an upper window, and saw the old woman rambling away from the schoolyard, still hacking the air with her knife and mauling the ground with the club. When she was well out of sight, I opened the door and found the steps slashed with knife marks and covered with limbs.

I tried to continue the lessons planned for that day, but after about an hour, when I felt confident the woman would not return, I decided to end classes early. My voice still quavering, I said, "School's dismissed for the day, children. Y'all stay close together goin' home and tell your folks what happened."

We gathered our belongings in haste, and I locked the school door. An older boy accompanied each group of smaller children, and I walked with the ones who lived closest to the Grahams' home.

After seeing the girls and boys safely inside their houses, I continued walking home alone, moving cautiously down the quiet and eerie road. Halfway home, to my horror, I saw the bewitched woman in the distance coming toward me. Hoping she had not seen me, I raced into the woods, not once thinking of snakes of which I am extremely afraid. Sprinting through the trees, I ducked under low limbs and maneuvered around underbrush until I reached the path between my boarding house and the bluff. I darted down the path and burst through the back door into the Grahams' kitchen, where Mrs. Graham stood ironing clothes.

"Goodness, child," she exclaimed, "what happened?"

"The witch," I managed to blurt out between gasps for air, "came to," I panted, "the school today."

"Drink this, dear." Mrs. Graham placed a cup of hot tea on the kitchen table and tenderly patted my shoulder. "You've had quite a scare. This will make you feel better."

With trembling hands, I lifted the teacup and sipped Mrs. Graham's own special recipe of cinnamon-clove spice tea.

"You're a good teacher, Elsie. You've done a wonderful job teachin' the children

at Shady Grove and you've helped Will Robison so much; but don't you think it might be wise to end the school term early and go on back to your family at Rankin Cove? There'll be another opportunity for you to teach next year."

I needed to think. After supper, I walked up the path to my favorite spot on Whitwell Mountain—the bluff. The events of the day seemed surreal against the quiet, magnificent beauty that encompassed me. The mountainsides blazed with color. A cool breeze rattled clusters of leaves dangling from the tree branches, and slender columns of smoke rose lazily from chimneys in the valley below the rocky precipice. Earthy scents from the mossy ground and dry foliage mingled with the smell of smoldering firewood.

"God is my refuge and strength" (Ps. 46:1), I remembered. Opening my Bible, I found Psalm 46 and read:

"God is our refuge and strength, a very present help in trouble,
Therefore we will not fear, though the earth should change
And though the mountains slip into the heart of the sea…
God is in the midst of her; she will not be moved;
God will help her when morning dawns." (Ps. 46:1-2,5)

"Father God, please help me overcome my fears. I desperately need You to grow my faith and help me to trust You no matter what troubles I face. Lord, You *are* my refuge and strength (Psa. 46:1). There is none like You, who rides the heavens to my help: the eternal God who shelters me in everlasting arms (Deut. 33:26-27). You gave me a job to do, and, by Your power, I'll finish it! Let me who loves You be like the rising of the sun in its might (Judg. 5:31b) and help my soul to march on with strength" (Judg. 5:21c).

The remainder of that week and the next were uneventful at Shady Grove. I moved with greater vigilance on my daily walks to the schoolhouse and found myself frequently looking out the front door during class time. At recess, I constantly surveyed the woods surrounding the schoolyard and roadway, keeping a watchful eye for unexpected prowlers. The children had little to say about the frightening visit from the strange woman, because, as I soon learned, she was an aunt to three of my students and no one wanted to embarrass them.

Then on Friday, as I called roll, the witch suddenly appeared in the doorway. Every eye locked upon her. The boys and girls froze into silent stone statues, and no one spoke or moved. My hands shook so fiercely that I clasped them behind my back in an effort to hide my fear from her as well as the children. I tried to speak, but no sound came from my mouth. In my mind, I repeated, "Lord, You are our strength and very present help in trouble" (Ps. 46:1).

The woman looked younger than I expected, maybe around forty years old. Her black hair was pinned back into a severe knot, revealing the long sticks wedged in her ears. I could see the sharp butcher knife and heavy club she carried in her bony hands. Scanning the room, her green eyes shifted from side to side, and then she said, "Howdy ma'am. May I have a drink of water to take my medicine with?"

I answered with a nod and a feeble, "Yes, ma'am," pointing to the water barrel by the door. To my surprise, her language and manners seemed to indicate she was educated.

She laid her weapons on the bench, took her medicine, and then asked, "May I speak to my nephew, Albert?"

When I nodded again, she turned to Albert and said, "Albert, you can tell your ma and pa I've been to the doctor, and he said I'm bewitched. That's what he said. He gave me some medicine and told me to wear these sticks in my ears to keep the witches away. They're after me."

The woman turned to pick up the knife and club but hesitated. "May I pray?" she asked.

After receiving my permission, she closed her eyes and prayed, "Dear God, bless this good teacher and these dear children who have been so kind to an old bewitched woman."

Picking up her weapons, she said, "Thank you and goodbye," and then vanished out the door.

I knew God had protected my students and me. When face to face with our greatest fear, the Lord of Hosts had been with us; the God of Jacob had proved to be our stronghold (Ps. 46:11). I picked up my Bible from my desk and read Isaiah 12:2 to the children, *"Behold, God is my salvation, I will trust and not be afraid; for the Lord God is my strength and song, and He has become my salvation."*

A few days after her visit to our classroom, once again the eccentric woman hurried past the school, this time carrying a small ax. She moved along the road in great haste, murmuring to herself and constantly looking back over her shoulder.

Later that day, her husband came to Shady Grove and asked if I had seen her pass. He had broad shoulders and large hands, calloused by hard work. A bulky bandage stained with blood covered his forehead, and a 12-gauge shotgun rested on his shoulder.

"She tried to kill me," he said. His voice sounded tired and sad.

The man found his tormented wife, and I was told he took her to a mental institution for help. From that day on, my students and I prayed for that poor woman and her family.

Reflections #5

POINTS to ponder

1. How did Elsie react when facing fear? _____

2. What is a good action plan when you face sudden calamity? _____

_____

3. Read 2 Chron. 16:9a and 1 John 4:4. God is _____ than what you fear and

He _____ supports those who belong to Him!

PEARLS from God's heart to yours

_____ (your name), have I not commanded you? Be strong and courageous!
Do not tremble… for the Lord your God is with you wherever you go (Josh. 1:9).

_____ (your name), I am your Rock and your fortress and your deliverer, your
God, your Rock in whom you take refuge; your Shield and the horn of your salvation, your
stronghold. Call upon Me who is worthy to be praised. I will save you from your enemies
(Ps. 18:2-3).

_____ (your name), don't despair; believe you will see My goodness. Wait for
Me, be strong and let your heart take courage; yes, wait for Me (Ps. 27:13-14).

PETITIONS from your heart to Jesus

_____

_____

_____

_____

Chapter 6
Fire!

*T*he fall weeks of the school term passed quickly, speeding toward the scheduled mid-December end. Brilliant colors of autumn faded to dull tones of raw umber and grayish-brown, a landscape drab and barren. The forest once closed with thick vegetation stood open and dormant.

Before the children arrived on those frosty winter mornings, I went to the school to stoke the fire in the stove and warm the classroom chilled by low overnight temperatures. Waking before daylight one brisk December day, I shivered as I hurried to dress and then opened the door to go to the kitchen for breakfast. Instead of the usual appetizing aroma of bacon frying on the stove and biscuits toasting in the oven, a pungent odor of wood smoke and loud voices from outside greeted me.

Running to the window, I saw Mr. and Mrs. Graham standing on the front porch. A neighbor, who had ridden over five miles on horseback, shouted to them, "Forest fire near Shady Grove! Forest fire!"

The arriving daylight revealed thick smoke hanging heavily in the air. The community rallied. Men, women, teens, and children, rakes and brooms in hand, rushed by foot, wagons, and horseback to the little schoolhouse—*my* sanctuary. I joined the fire fighting forces along with Gladys and the entire Graham family.

Mr. Robison and his son were among the first to reach Shady Grove. When we arrived, I saw Will sweeping fallen leaves away from the school with a stubby broom. I had learned to love that young man who frequented the schoolyard during recess to play baseball with the boys. When my students returned to class, he never failed to embrace me with a big ol' bear hug before trotting happily down the path toward home.

The mountain neighbors worked feverishly for hours clearing dry leaves and limbs away from the building and patting out sparks from burning trees carried by the wind into the schoolyard. Working the hand pump on the well up and down, up and down, the boys and girls

filled bucket after bucket with water. They drenched the wooden boards of the landing and steps as well as the ground surrounding our cherished school.

By late morning, a cleared area encircled the schoolhouse, but flames seemed to be closing in from every direction. The menfolk agreed the situation was becoming too dangerous to stay at the school, so Mr. Graham rang the school bell signaling that the assembly needed to head back to their homes.

We left quickly, picking our way through burning leaves that covered the road. The afternoon sky grew darker from rain clouds building above the dense blanket of smoke. Before the Grahams, Gladys, and I could get home, raindrops began hitting the ground, hissing as water touched hot embers. The large drops grew to a steady downpour, dowsing the blazing forest. Shady Grove would be safe.

"Do not fear, for I have redeemed you; I have called you by name; you are Mine. When you pass through the waters, I will be with you; and through the rivers, they will not overflow you. When you walk through the fire, you will not be scorched, nor will the flame burn you. For I am the Lord your God" (Isa. 43:1-3), Gladys quoted exuberantly from the Old Testament as we tramped along the mud-paved road. Although soaked to the bone and freezing cold, gratitude to God for sending rain in our hour of need warmed my soul. I held Mary Grace's small hand in mine, and together, in joy and thanksgiving to God, we sang:

"Thro' many dangers, toils and snares, I have already come;
'Tis grace hath bro't me, safe thus far, and grace will lead me home.
The Lord has promised good to me, His word my hope secures;
He will my shield and portion be as long as life endures." [3]

Inside the cottage, Gladys and the girls hung wet clothes in front of the fireplace to dry, and Mr. Graham worked to secure windows and doors from the effects of the storm. In the kitchen, Mrs. Graham and I prepared a late lunch. While I stirred a pot of soup made from vegetables Mrs. Graham had canned from her summer garden, she poured cornbread batter into a heavy iron skillet sizzling with hot bacon grease. The two of us worked well together, and, in no time, the meal was ready.

"Nothing makes food taste better than a hard day's work," Mr. Graham commented after dipping his second bowl of soup. On his way back to his chair, that tough, yet tender, man paused by his wife and kissed her cheek. Godly love bonded the Graham family. Their affection for and commitment to one another reflected the character of that mountain community I had grown to love and respect.

---

[3] AMAZING GRACE, Words, John Newton, 1779. Tune, Virginia Harmony, 1831.

The storm continued throughout the afternoon. Tall trees swayed in the blustery wind like wooden masts on a rocking ship. By evening, the temperature had dropped drastically changing raindrops into white flurries—the first snow of winter.

Reflecting on the events of the day, I curled in a rocker by the fireplace for a long while after the others went to bed. The oak logs hissed and crackled in the heat of blue and yellow flames. I sat mesmerized by the red glow of hot coals beneath the grate and jumped when a sudden POP launched a spray of glittering sparks up the chimney.

Before teaching at Shady Grove, I believed I could accomplish anything with help from God alone. Watching the Grahams' neighbors pull together and work as a team to save my school helped me realize the need for God *and* community.

I opened my Bible to Ecclesiastes 4:9-10,12 and in the dimming firelight read, *"Two are better than one because they have a good return for their labor. For if either of them falls, the one will lift up his companion... a cord of three strands is not quickly torn apart."* On that wintry night, King Solomon's proverb penetrated my heart as never before.

I added a log to the fire before heading to bed and then peeked through the lace curtains to discover a snow-globe-like wonderland. Crystal flakes, swirling and dancing in the darkness, had begun to stick, covering the branches of the Fraser firs and the ground. Powdery, white front porch steps looked as if a baker had sprinkled them with confectioner's sugar.

In my bed, I felt an overpowering sense of God's peace and happiness as I snuggled beneath three heavy quilts. It was hard for me to believe the school term would end the following week. I prayed for my students and our remaining time together and then drifted off into sweet sleep (Prov. 3:24).

Reflections #6

POINTS to ponder

1. Which do you like better, working alone or with others? _____

2. What did Elsie learn about teamwork? _____

   Read Heb.10:24-25. What is one advantage of working with others as opposed to working

   alone?_____

3. Read 1 Cor. 12:12-27. Believers are the _____ of Christ: one body with many

   members, each member performing its duty but all members working _____.

PEARLS from God's heart to yours

_____ (your name), encourage one another and build each other up
(1 Thess. 5:11).

_____ (your name), two are better than one because they have a good return
for their labor. If either of them falls, the other will lift up his companion...A cord of three
strands is not quickly torn apart (Eccles. 4:9-12).

My whole body of believers is joined and held together. When each part is working properly, it
makes the whole body grow so that it is built up in love (Eph. 4:16).

PETITIONS from your heart to Jesus

_____

_____

_____

_____

Chapter 7
Lessons Learned by the Teacher

The last test taken, the final grade calculated, the last day of school ended.

Albert, the last student to leave the classroom, stopped at the door and said, "I love you, Miss Thomas."

A flood of emotions swept over me—love for my students, gratitude to God, thankfulness for the accomplishments, and sadness that my first teaching assignment was over. My lips curved to a smile as I imagined Will, perched like a squirrel on the crossbeam above my head, but I cringed a bit recollecting him labeled as an "unbalanced boy." Pulling a sheet of stationary from my satchel, I dipped my pen in the well of indigo blue ink and wrote a letter to the youngest of my three older sisters:

Dearest Bess,

I hope this letter finds you and Harry well and settled into your new home in Chattanooga.

The school term at Shady Grove ended today. My heart is full and I long to share my thoughts with you, dear sister. Five months ago, I arrived as a stranger on Whitwell Mountain. Very quickly, however, I became immersed into a community where I found consolation from my God, comfort from my boarding family, acceptance from my neighbors, and purpose from the children I was so privileged to teach.

I am certain I learned more lessons during these months than my students. My eyes beheld my Teacher and my ears heard His voice behind me say, "This is the way, walk in it" (Isa. 30:20-21). God taught me that He truly is sufficient for all circumstances and trained me to face my fears with courage and fortitude. Through my students and a special young friend named Will Robison, He revealed to me the beauty of humility and the ugliness of prejudices. God showed me it is through perseverance and working with others that one finishes strong.

Tomorrow I travel back to our farm in Rankin Cove. I am eager to see Mama and Papa but I will greatly miss the Grahams, my friends, and especially my students.

I look forward to seeing you and Harry when you visit Christmas Day. Take care, my precious Bess, and give my love to your sweet husband.

With deepest affections,
Elsie

I folded the letter and put it in my satchel. My eyes traveled from desk to desk envisioning the faces of my beloved students. In the uncharacteristic silence of that classroom, I missed the harmonic symphony of children's voices. Slipping from my chair, I knelt on the clean plank floor that Oliver had swept for me before leaving that day. Looking toward God, I prayed:

Dear Heavenly Father,

*You **have** made known to me the path of life; in Your presence **has been** fullness of joy; in Your right hand there **truly are** pleasures forever (Ps. 16:11). I praise You, Almighty God, my Provider and my Protector.*

O Father, forgive me for allowing anxiety and fears to haunt me those first weeks of the school term. Forgive me for judging ones I did not know nor understand.

Thank You for my dear students. Please help them to remember the lessons they learned this school year, from both books and life. I pray they will always love You, obey Your voice, and hold fast to You (Deut. 30:20). Please bless the Grahams for the kindness they have shown me and be with my friend, Gladys, keeping her safe as she travels home tomorrow.

Lord, You told us that in this world we will have tribulation but to take courage, You have overcome the world (John 16:33). Thank You, Father God, for helping me overcome the fears and challenges I faced at Shady Grove, thank You for the lessons You have taught this teacher, and thank You for enabling me to see this school term through to completion.

To You, O God, be the glory, honor, praise, dominion, and thanksgiving forever and ever.

In Jesus' name I pray,

Amen

Rising to my feet, I picked up my satchel, walked out of the schoolhouse, and locked the door behind me: the first teacher to complete a full term at Shady Grove in five years.

The following summer, the county superintendent asked me to return to Shady Grove. However, by God's providence, I elected to take a teaching position at Hales Bar where I met and later married Oscar Franklin Brazelle.

But that's another story.

Author's Reflections

Dear Reader,

Thank you for reading *The Schoolhouse*. I hope my grandmother's story has encouraged you to depend more deeply on God and inspired you to persevere through difficult circumstances and to finish strong the task at hand. To finish LIFE strong, however, is of far greater value than merely completing an assignment well.

I believe God had *you* on His heart when He whispered, "Jill, it's time to write her story." Although I may not know your name, as I wrote, I prayed for you.

Before you were even born, God knew your name. He knew you (and I) would make mistakes; He knew we would sin. Since the payment for sin is death and separation from God forever, He loves you so much that God sent His Son, Jesus, to pay the death penalty for you. Over two thousand years ago, Jesus died on a cross in your place so that you may receive forgiveness for your sins and the free gift of never-ending, eternal life with God.

I pray that, like Elsie in this story, you have a personal relationship with Jesus. I hope you talk to Him through prayer, listen to Him through His Word, and trust Him to meet your every need. If Jesus truly is your Savior and Lord, He will rescue you from every evil deed and one day bring you safely to His heavenly kingdom (2 Tim. 4:18).

I also pray that every day of your life, you will fight the good fight, keep the faith, and finish strong, the course of life that God has set before you (2 Tim. 4:7).

Jill Watson Glassco

LifeHouse Publishing

Bringing Life to Books

Do you need a speaker?

Do you want Jill Glassco to speak to your group or event? Then contact Larry Davis at: (623) 337-8710 or email: ldavis@intermediapr.com or use the contact form at: www.intermediapr.com.

Whether you want to purchase bulk copies of *The Schoolhouse* or buy another book for a friend, get it now at: www.imprbooks.com.

If you have a book that you would like to publish, contact Terry Whalin, Publisher, at Intermedia Publishing Group, (623) 337-8710 or email: twhalin@intermediapub.com or use the contact form at: www.intermediapub.com.